Dick Bruna

Sophie's Toys

Collins

SOPHIE'S TOYS

First published in Great Britain 1989 by William Collins Sons & Co Ltd,
8 Grafton Street, London W1X 3LA

0 00 191103 1

Exclusively arranged and produced by De Boekerij/Van Goor bv, Amsterdam
Illustrations Dick Bruna, © copyright Mercis bv, 1988

Printed and bound by Brepols Fabrieken NV, Belgium